STAR WARS
GENERAL GRIEVOUS

THE EVENTS IN THIS SERIES TAKE PLACE
TWO YEARS AFTER THE BATTLE OF GEONOSIS.

STAR WARS®
GENERAL GRIEVOUS

SCRIPT CHUCK DIXON   PENCILS RICK LEONARDI   INKS MARK PENNINGTON

COLORS CHRIS CHUCKRY   WITH MICHELLE MADSEN   AND DAN JACKSON

LETTERS DAVE LANPHEAR   COVER ART PAOLO PUENTE

TITAN BOOKS

PUBLISHER MIKE RICHARDSON

EDITOR DAVE LAND

ASSISTANT EDITOR KATIE MOODY

COLLECTION DESIGNER JOSHUA ELLIOTT

ART DIRECTOR LIA RIBACCHI

SPECIAL THANKS TO SUE ROSTONI, LELAND CHEE,
AND AMY GARY AT LUCAS LICENSING.

PUBLISHED BY
Titan Books
A Division of Titan Publishing Group Ltd.
144 Southwark Street
London SE1 0UP

www.titanbooks.com   www.starwars.com

A CIP catalogue record for this title is available from the British Library.

This edition first published: February 2006
ISBN: 1-84576-109-X

2 4 6 8 10 9 7 5 3 1

Printed in Italy.

"THINGS FELL APART *RAPIDLY*.

"THE RESCUE MISSION TO *VANDOS* WAS TO BE SIMPLE...

"...TO LAND AHEAD OF THE APPROACHING SEPARATIST INVASION FLEET AND BRING OUT *AMBASSADOR QUIYYEN*.

"WE FOUND INSTEAD A LARGE FORCE OF *BATTLE DROIDS* AWAITING US.

"THE AMBASSADOR WAS THE *BAIT* FOR THE TRAP...

"A TRAP SPRUNG UPON US BY AN *ENEMY* WHO HAS BEEN GROWING IN INFAMY.

"WE HAVE ALL HEARD HIS NAME AGAIN AND AGAIN IN RECENT DAYS.

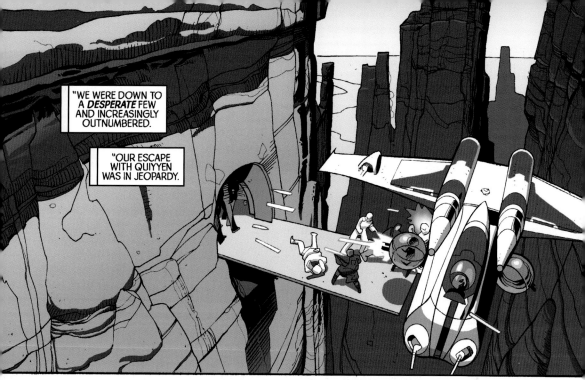

"WE WERE DOWN TO A *DESPERATE* FEW AND INCREASINGLY OUTNUMBERED.

"OUR ESCAPE WITH QUIYYEN WAS IN JEOPARDY.

"MY JEDI MASTER, *T'CHOOKA D'OON,* STEPPED INTO THE BREACH."

T'CHOOKA! NO!

"SKILLED AND COURAGEOUS, HE ACQUITTED HIMSELF WELL.

"IN THE END IT WAS BUT A FORLORN HOPE.

"THERE IS NO QUESTION THAT MASTER T'CHOOKA WAS A *FEARLESS* WARRIOR.

"THE FORCE WAS *STRONG* IN HIM ON VANDOS.

"HIS SKILLS WERE GREAT.

"BUT NOT ENOUGH.

"*GRIEVOUS* MADE SHORT WORK OF HIM.

"THERE WAS *NOTHING* TO BE DONE.

"THE AMBASSADOR WAS SAFELY ABOARD.

"FOR ALL OUR CASUALTIES, WE HAD SUCCEEDED.

"TO DELAY WITHDRAWAL WOULD JEOPARDIZE *EVERYTHING.*

"IT WAS *GRIEVOUS* WE FACED.

"THERE IS NO MISTAKING HIM."

"JUST AS THERE IS NO MISTAKING HIS *DANGER* TO THE REPUBLIC..."

"...AND TO THE *JEDI ORDER*."

HE HAS MURDERED *HUNDREDS* OF OUR BROTHERS AND SISTERS.

A *KALEE* HE ONCE WAS. FLESH AND BLOOD WAS HE.

WHATEVER HIS ORIGINS, HE IS AN *ABOMINATION* WROUGHT BY THE GEONOSIANS AND THE SITH.

THE NEAR-INDESTRUCTABILITY OF A BATTLE DROID WEDDED TO THE SKILLS OF A *DEADLY* WARRIOR.

COUNT DOOKU HAS FOUND A WORTHY ALLY.

HE BESTED SO MANY GREAT JEDI AT HYPORI AND ELSEWHERE, TAKING THEIR *LIGHTSABERS* AS PRIZES.

TROUBLING. TROUBLING THIS IS.

EXPEDIENT IT IS? CONCERN HIMSELF WITH EASE A JEDI DOES NOT.

COLD VENGEANCE IT IS. THE PATH TO THE DARK SIDE IT IS.

MASTER YODA, I ASSURE YOU THAT IT IS NOT REVENGE THAT MOTIVATES ME.

I ONLY THINK THAT ONE LIFE MAY BE TRADED FOR THE LIVES OF MANY.

PASSION IN YOUR VOICE THERE IS. ANGER BELOW THE SURFACE ROILS. RECALL YOUR TRAINING YOU MUST.

OUTSIDE YOUR NEW MASTER WAITS, FLYNN KYBO.

WITH YOUR TRAINING CONCERN YOURSELF. GRIEVOUS' FATE FOR THE COUNCIL TO DETERMINE, IT IS.

PADAWAN KYBO?

YES?

I AM TO BE YOUR MASTER.

I AM *PLEASED* AND HONORED.

I AM Z'MEER BOTHU.

I LOOK FORWARD TO *GUIDING* YOU IN THE WAYS OF THE *FORCE*.

ARE WE TO BEGIN MY TRAINING NOW?

YES. AND YOUR FIRST LESSON IS IN...

"...SILENT CONTEMPLATION."

MASTER 'MEER?

WE HAVE BEEN *CONTEMPLATING* FOR HOURS. WHAT AM I SUPPOSED TO CONTEMPLATE *UPON*?

MASTER?

Z'MEER IS *DEEP* IN HER TRANCE, FLYNN KYBO.

IF YOU *BELIEVE* IN THIS ACTION THEN WE WILL MEET AGAIN.

THE CANTINA ON HUSKER SQUARE?

TOMORROW EVENING, THEN.

MAY THE FORCE BE WITH US *ALL*.

SUCH *REBELLION* EVEN FOR ONE SO YOUNG.

UH?

BUT I THOUGHT YOU WERE--

IN MEDITATION. NOT *ASLEEP*.

WHAT AM I TO *DO* WITH YOU, PADAWAN?

YOU QUESTION YOUR BETTERS. YOU RESIST THEIR *WISDOM*.

WILL YOU TRY AND *STOP* ME?

I WILL NOT.

WILL YOU TELL THE COUNCIL?

THEY WILL KNOW WITHOUT A WORD FROM ME.

GO, PADAWAN. DO AS YOU MUST.

BUT KNOW THAT YOU WILL *NEVER* BE OFFERED A PLACE AMONG THE *JEDI* AGAIN.

"AND YOU MAY HAVE CAUSE TO *REGRET* YOUR BOLDNESS."

BZOW

BZOW

BZOW

TOOM TOOM

THIS SHIP *STINKS* OF FISH. OR SO I WOULD *IMAGINE.*

THE *MON CALAMARI* ARE SUCH A DISGUSTING SPECIES.

THE SHIP IS TAKEN, *GENERAL GRIEVOUS.*

A *JEDI WARRIOR* IS ABOARD. HE HAS BEEN SPARED AS YOU ORDERED.

LET US *INSPECT* HIM, EH?

AN *ABYSSIN.*

GRIEVOUS.

A *LONG W* FROM THE D OF BYS

WHAT *DO* V YO

SHA ENGAGE YOUR *C* FORM COM

MASTER PH'TON, CAN WE EXPECT *SUPPORT* FROM ALDERAAN ITSELF?

WE WILL NOT. ALDERAAN DOES NOT HAVE A *SIGNIFICANT* MILITARY CAPABILITY.

THEY RELY UPON *US* TO DO THEIR *FIGHTING*.

READY YOURSELF FOR *COMBAT*.

AND MAY *THE FORCE* BE WITH YOU.

YOU SPOKE OUT OF TURN, PADAWAN.

I ONLY--

ONLY CHALLENGED THE *AUTHORITY* OF YOUR BETTERS.

WERE YOU SCOLDING *HIM* OR *ME*, MASTER Z'MEER?

PADAWAN KYBO, YOU WILL BE *DESERTING* BEFORE AN ATTACK.

YOU WISH TO *DISCOURAGE* ME, MASTER?

NO, I ONLY HIGHLIGHT THE *GRAVITY* OF YOUR DECISION.

I SACRIFICE MY PLACE IN THE ORDER FOR A *GREATER* GOOD.

MY *PATH* IS CHOSEN...

"I FOLLOW IT NOW TO THE *END*."

DID YOU HEAR THAT?

A *SKITTERING* NOISE?

SOME KIND OF *VERMIN*.

IT CAME FROM OVER HERE.

VOOSH

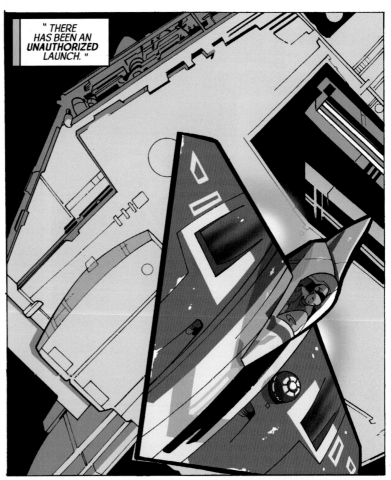

" THERE HAS BEEN AN **UNAUTHORIZED** LAUNCH. "

SINGLE PASSENGER CRAFT.

IT DEPARTED BAY NINE **WITHOUT** CLEARANCE.

A **KUAT** INTERCEPTOR.

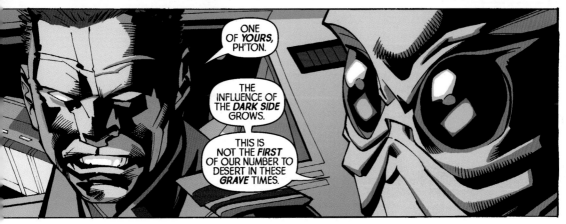

ONE OF **YOURS**, PH'TON.

THE INFLUENCE OF THE **DARK SIDE** GROWS.

THIS IS NOT THE **FIRST** OF OUR NUMBER TO DESERT IN THESE **GRAVE** TIMES.

"IT WILL **NOT** BE THE LAST.

"ONLY DAYS AGO A PAIR OF **JEDI** WENT MISSING WITHOUT LEAVE."

FINAL APPROACH TO **BRYNDAR** SURFACE.

I HAVE NEVER HEARD OF THIS **WORLD**.

FEW HAVE. **BRYNDAR** IS FAR OFF THE **NORMAL** SHIPPING LANES.

THE PERFECT PORT FOR **SPICE SMUGGLERS** AND **CRIMINALS**.

AND **RENEGADE** JEDI.

BUT IT IS IMPORTANT THAT WE KEEP OUR **TRUE NATURE** A SECRET, CODI.

AS YOU COMMAND, MASTER TONE.

I HAVE NO WISH TO **JEOPARDIZE** OU MISSION...

"...OR THE [LI]VES OF OUR COMRADES."

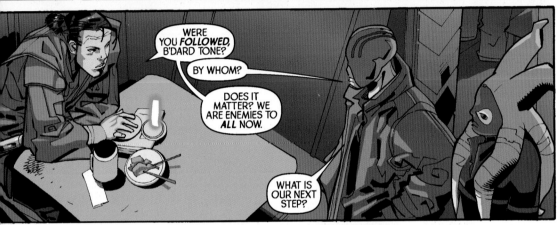

WERE YOU *FOLLOWED*, B'DARD TONE?

BY WHOM?

DOES IT MATTER? WE ARE ENEMIES TO *ALL* NOW.

WHAT IS OUR NEXT STEP?

TO FIND *GENERAL GRIEVOUS*. MY ASTROMECH IS MONITORING FEDERATION SUBSPACE COMMS.

HE COULD BE ON ANY OF A *HUNDRED* WORLDS.

HE SHOULD NOT BE THAT *DIFFICULT* TO FIND.

AFTER ALL, MASTER B'DARD..

TO BE CONTINUED...

ENCODED SUB-SPACE
TRANSMISSION:

TRADE FEDERATION
CODE MAXIMA.

THE PLANET
GENTES IN THE
ANOAT SYSTEM.

HOME PLANET TO
THE SPECIES KNOWN
AS UGNAUGHTS.

OPERATIONS HAVE
BEGUN TO TAKE
THIS KEY POSITION.

AS A SPECIES, THE
UGNAUGHTS
CONCENTRATE
THEIR EFFORTS ON
MANUFACTURE.

RESISTANCE IS
ANTICIPATED
TO BE MINIMAL.

GENTES IS RICH IN
MINERAL WEALTH.

IT HAS MANY MINING AND
INDUSTRIAL FACILITIES.

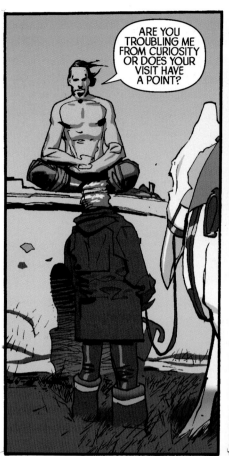

ARE YOU TROUBLING ME FROM CURIOSITY OR DOES YOUR VISIT HAVE A POINT?

MY NAME IS STELLSKARD OF THE BANYHAR COMBINE. WORD IS THAT YOU'RE LOOKING FOR GENERAL GRIEVOUS.

WE SEEK VOLUNTEERS FO A MISSION TO FIND HIM.

AND KILL HIM, I HOPE.

IF THERE' ENOUGH A AMONGST MACHINE L TO KILL

WE'VE HAD LITTLE FORTUNE.

YOU'RE LOOKING IN THE WRONG PLACE.

Hm.

AND I SUPPOSE YOU HAVE A SUGGESTION.

FOR ONE, LET'S GET OUT OF THIS WIND.

FOR THE OTHER, I KNO PEOPLE WHO HARBOR MO HATRED FOR GRIEVOUS TH YOU CAN IMAGINE.

THANKS TO MY UNERRING BATTLE PLAN WE HAVE TAKEN THIS PLANET WITH A MINIMUM OF DAMAGE...

...TO EITHER ITS MANUFACTURING FACILITIES OR WORKING POPULATION.

IT IS MY UNDERSTANDING THAT UGNAUGHTS ARE PARTICULARLY PRODUCTIVE WORKERS.

SO IT IS SAID, GENERAL GRIEVOUS.

LESS THAN TWENTY PERCENT DAMAGE TO ASSEMBLY PLANTS AND MINING OPERATIONS.

AND THE POPULATION?

REDUNDANT. THE GEONOSIANS FIND IT MORE EFFICIENT TO USE MACHINES TO BUILD MACHINES.

WE MAY NEED A FEW TO HELP IN RETOOLING THE FACTORIES TO THE GEONOSIAN NEEDS.

FOLLOWING THAT, THEY ARE OF LITTLE USE TO US.

EXCEPT PERHAPS AS AN OBJECT LESSON.

HE SAYS HE CAN HELP US, MASTER TONE.

HELP HIMSELF, MORE LIKELY. LOOK AT HIM. HE'D BETRAY US IN A HEARTBEAT.

I MAY LOOK WORN, JEDI. BUT I'LL BET I'VE SEEN MORE ACTION AGAINST THE TRADE FEDERATION THAN YOU.

HANG ABOUT THIS PLANET MUCH LONGER AND YOU WILL BE SOLD TO THE CONFEDERACY.

WE HEARD THAT THE INHABITANTS OF THIS SECTOR HATED THE TRADE FEDERATION.

BUT NOT ONE HAS STEPPED FORWARD TO AID US.

HATE AND FEAR, JEDI. THE FEAR OUTWEIGHS THE HATE.

SOME WRETCHES WOULD JUST AS SOON HAND YOU OVER TO CURRY FAVOR WITH THE MONEYMEN.

THEN WHERE MIGHT WE GO TO FIND ALLIES?

A PLACE WHERE FURY BURNS BRIGHT FOR THE TRADERS AND THEIR MACHINES.

I CAN TAKE YOU TO THE HEART OF THAT FIRE...

NO NEED TO TROUBLE YOURSELF OVER THEM, DOOKU.

I HAVE PLANS FOR THOSE JEDI PUPS.

THEY SHOULD BE TURNED OVER TO THE SITH.

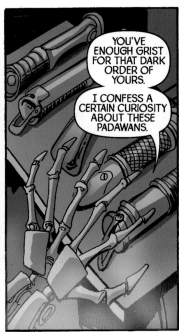

YOU'VE ENOUGH GRIST FOR THAT DARK ORDER OF YOURS.

I CONFESS A CERTAIN CURIOSITY ABOUT THESE PADAWANS.

AND CURIOSITY ONE OF TH RARE TRAIT HAVE LEF

VERY WELL. YOU MAY HOLL THE CHILDREN FOR NOW.

BUT THEY ARE PRECIOUS, FOR THE FORCE LIVES IN THEM.

AND WITH IT THE SOURCE OF MUCH POTENTIAL DARK ENERGY THAT MIGHT BE HARNESSED FOR THE SITH.

LOTS OF SCRAMBLED SUB-SPACE CHATTER. THE CODE IS A NEW ONE.

THAT MEANS IT'S HIGH-LEVE THAT MEANS CONFEDERACY

I'M SURE I CAN BREAK IT IT'S A RANDOM SUBSTITUTION CODE.

A SEPARATIST CODE. I RECOGNIZE IT. IT'S MATHEMATIC AS WELL AS PHONETIC.

YOUR EQUIPMENT IS OUTDATED. ARE YOU CERTAIN YOU CAN BREAK A CODE LIKE THIS?

ABSOLUTELY!

IF YOU GIVE ME SOME TIME.

A YEAR, MAYBE.

PERHAPS I CAN HELP.

CB-3D, COULD YOU ASSIST US?

BEE-*BIP!*

I'M NOT SURE ABOUT THIS. MY SYSTEM IS VERY TEMPERAMENTAL AND--

RELAX, RINI. THEY'RE ON OUR SIDE.

SKIDDA SKIDDA -*BIP!*

Boooo-ip-ip-ip-Beeeee

PADAWANS?

WHAT IS THIS MENTION OF PADAWANS?

YOU ARE DISTRESSED, FLYNN KYBO.

A SUB-SPACE EXCHANGE. CB-3D IDENTIFIES ONE OF THE PARTICIPANTS AS GENERAL GRIEVOUS.

THERE IS MENTION OF PADAWANS AND THE SITH LORDS.

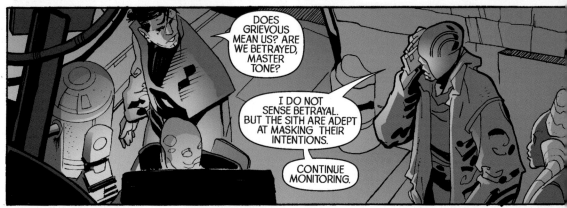

DOES GRIEVOUS MEAN US? ARE WE BETRAYED, MASTER TONE?

I DO NOT SENSE BETRAYAL. BUT THE SITH ARE ADEPT AT MASKING THEIR INTENTIONS.

CONTINUE MONITORING.

IT IS THAT ENERGY THAT INTERESTS ME, COUNT DOOKU.

CAN THE POWER OF THE DARK SIDE LYING DORMANT IN THESE PADAWANS BE WEDDED WITH GEONOSIAN TECHNOLOGY?

AS YOU ARE WEDDED, GRIEVOUS.

PRECISELY.

I SHARE YOUR CURIOSITY IN THIS EXPERIMENT.

CARRY ON, GENERAL.

THAT'S IT. TRANSMISSION ENDS.

AND THE SOURCE OF GRIEVOUS' TRANSMISSIONS?

THE ISON CORRIDOR. SOMEWHERE NEAR THE ANOAT SYSTEM.

THAT'S AS CLOSE AS I COULD TAG IT.

ANOAT HAS THREE HABITABLE WORLDS AND COUNTLESS MOONS AND SATELLITES.

IT WOULD TAKE A LIFETIME TO FIND GRIEVOUS.

AND BY THAT TIME HE'D BE LONG GONE.

UNLESS...

OUR WAR WITH THE TRADE FEDERATION WAS A SHORT ONE.

BUT WE MANAGED TO CAPTURE SOME OF THEIR EQUIPMENT BEFORE IT WAS OVER.

WE NEED SOMETHING THAT CAN SCAN THE ANOAT SYSTEM WITHOUT DRAWING ATTENTION TO US.

AND QUICKLY.

LIKE THIS?

IT'S A TRADE FEDERATION PROBE. I HAVE THREE OF THEM UP AND RUNNING.

THEY CAN SCAN IN A DOZEN DIFFERENT MODES AND--

I AM MORE THAN FAMILIAR WITH THEM.

I SAW THEM FIRST IN THE DAYS BEFORE HYPORI. THEY SEARCH FOR TARGETS. RELENTLESS. TIRELESS.

HOW CAN WE BE CERTAIN THEY DO NOT CONTAIN HIDDEN PROGRAMMING THAT WILL BETRAY US?

CB-3D CAN MAKE SURE THEIR MEMORIES ARE WIPED.

WHAT BETTER WAY TO FIND GRIEVOUS?

HE HAS TO TRANSMIT TO STAY IN CONTROL OF HIS UNITS.

RINI'S RIGHT. IT'S OUR BEST OPTION.

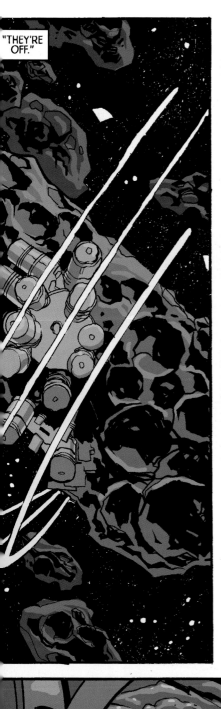

"THEY'RE OFF."

THEY SHOULD BEGIN SIGNALING BACK IN A FEW DAYS.

THEN WE CAN NARROW THE HUNT FOR GRIEVOUS.

OR LEAD HIM RIGHT BACK TO US.

IF OUR LOCATION IS NOT ALREADY KNOWN TO HIM.

CHILDREN.

PERHAPS YOU WONDER WHAT FATE I HAVE PLANNED FOR YOU.

UNNH!

A DIVERTING ENTERTAINMENT.

YOU'VE SHOWN ME SOMETHING, LITTLE ONE.

NOW ALLOW ME MY OWN DEMONSTRATION OF POWER.

THE POWER I HOLD OVER THE LIFE AND DEATH OF EVERY BEING IN THIS SYSTEM.

UNH!

THE POWER OF MY WORD.

TO BE CONTINUE

"LIFEFORM PROFILE BELOW PROJECTED LEVELS.

"THERE'S BEEN A MASSACRE HERE."

I HAVE A LOCK!

TRANSMISSION IN MAXIMA! SAME SIGNATURE!

"IT'S GRIEVOUS.

"ALL THREE PROBOTS ARE FIXED ON THE SOURCE."

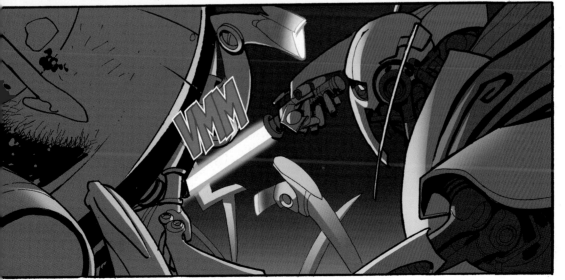

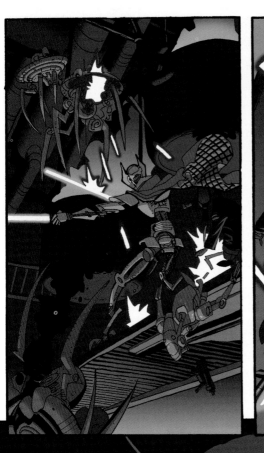

SOMEONE WANTS ME ELIMINATED, NEIMOIDIAN.

A BETRAYAL FROM YOUR FELLOW MERCHANTS?

VMM

OR PERHAPS DARTH TYRANUS HAS TIRED OF ME.

WHAM

OOH!

OOH!

GAH!

VCHOOM

OH, THANK YOU, GENERAL! THANK YOU!

YOUR LIFE IS A GIFT I MAY RESCIND, NEIMOIDIAN.

IF I DISCOVER THAT YOUR BROTHER BUSINESSMEN WERE BEHIND THIS...

"...YOU'LL WISH I'D LEFT YOU TO THE FIRES OF THE FORGE."

CONCENTRATE, PADAWANS...

BRING THE FORCE TO BEAR.

REACH OUT WITH YOUR WILL.

IT'S NO GOOD, ALLARA. WE'RE NOT STRONG ENOUGH.

WE'LL NEVER GET THAT DOOR OPEN WITH THAT ATTITUDE, BANZ.

OPEN THE DOOR? IS THAT WHAT WE WERE DOING?

HUSH, TAK-TAK!

TNK

IT'S A DATA PROBE!

I DON'T SENSE DANGER FROM IT.

HELLO?

TEK TEK

OH!

SENSE ANY DANGER NOW, ALLARA?

RRRMBBBLL

NERBER! NERBER!

DOES ANYONE SPEAK UGNAUGHT?

I THINK HE WANTS US TO COME WITH HIM!

THE FORCE IS WITH US!

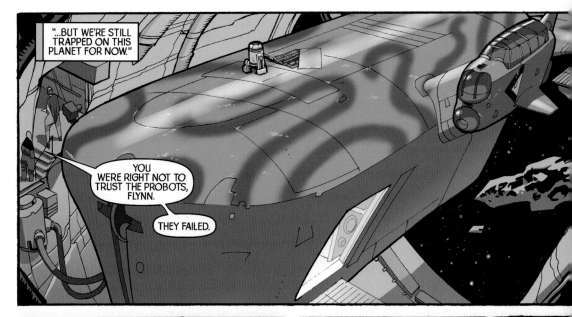

"...BUT WE'RE STILL TRAPPED ON THIS PLANET FOR NOW."

YOU WERE RIGHT NOT TO TRUST THE PROBOTS, FLYNN.

THEY FAILED.

THEY HAD NO CHANCE AGAINST GRIEVOUS. NO SIMPLE MACHINE COULD DEFEAT HIM.

WE'VE ONLY SERVED TO WARN HIM. HE'LL BE ON HIS GUARD NOW, RINI.

THEN I HOPE THE TRADE FEDERATION CODES I HAVE WILL GET US THROUGH.

OTHERWISE, THIS IS GOING TO BE A REAL SHORT TRIP.

FLYNN, WE HAVE ASKED FOR VOLUNTEERS AMONG THE BANVHAR MINERS.

I DID NOT HIDE FROM THEM THE GRIM POSSIBILITIES OR THE NEAR CERTAINTY THAT WE WILL NEVER RETURN.

SO, HOW MANY ARE COMING ALONG, MASTER TONE?

ALL OF THEM.

COME ALONG, CB-3D.

BEE-*THROOP!*

YOU'LL BE NEEDED IF OUR TRAVEL CODES ARE OUTDATED.

YOU KNOW, EVEN IF WE SUCCEED, WE WILL NEVER BE WELCOMED BACK BY THE JEDI ORDER.

AND, SHOULD WE FAIL, NO ONE WILL MOURN US.

SO LONG AS GRIEVOUS IS SLAIN, OUR FATES MATTER LITTLE, MASTER.

WITHIN DAYS OF LANDING FORCES ON THE PLANET WE HAVE SUPRESSED RESISTANCE ENTIRELY.

BY ANNIHILATING THE NATIVE POPULATION.

I FIND THAT THE MOST EFFICIENT FORM OF SUPPRESSION.

THE MANUFACTURING FACILITIES SUFFERED LITTLE DAMAGE AND ARE BACK TO FULL PRODUCTION.

INCLUDING AN EXPERIMENT OF YOUR OWN, GENERAL.

YES.

A MECHANIZED ARMOR FRAME MUCH LIKE MY OWN.

BUT CHAMBERED FOR MY...YOUNG CHARGES.

THE PADAWANS YOU CAPTURED.

A CREATURE ADEPT IN THE FORCE AND WEDDED TO THE ULTIMATE IN TECHNOLOGY WOULD BE A FORMIDABLE WARRIOR.

THAT WOULD NECESSITATE SOME ALTERATIONS, NO?

THE REMOVAL OF CERTAIN REDUNDANT ORGANS, AND AMPUTATIONS.

IS THERE PAIN INVOLVED?

IT IS NOTHING, COMPARED TO THE BENEFITS.

I SPEAK FROM EXPERIENCE.

I COULD ASSIST YOU.

SO LONG AS YOU DO NOT REMOVE THEM FROM MY CARE.

NOT UNLESS COUNT DOOKU SO ORDERS.

THEY ARE SPIRITED, BUT I BELIEVE THAT...

WHERE HAVE THEY GONE, GENERAL?

NOT FAR, COMMANDER.

NOT FAR.

WHERE ARE THEY TAKING US?

I DON'T CARE, SO LONG AS IT'S AWAY FROM THAT CELL.

I THOUGHT GRIEVOUS KILLED ALL THE UGNAUGHTS.

THE GENERAL ISN'T INFALLIBLE, BANZ.

HE'S NO FOOL, EITHER.

WE'RE BEING FOLLOWED.

TARGET SIGHTED. MISSION PRIORITY ONE.

AWAITING FURTHER ORDERS.

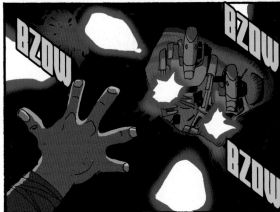

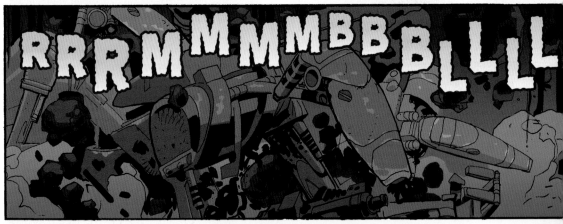

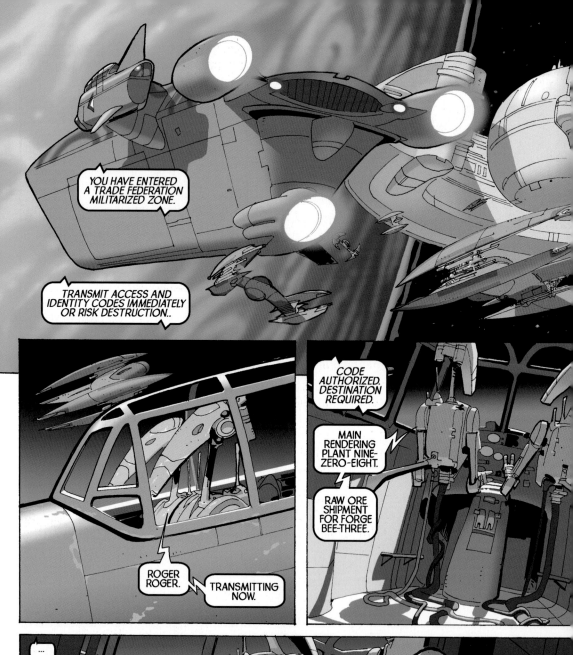

OUR RUSE HAS SUCCEEDED. THE CODES ARE RECENT ENOUGH TO PASS BUT TOO OLD NOT TO BE QUESTIONED.

WE ARE BEING DIRECTED TO THE FEDERATION CUSTOMS CENTER FOR CLEARANCE.

THAT PLACES US CLOSE TO OUR LAST KNOWN LOCATION FOR GRIEVOUS.

DEATH TO GRIEVOUS!

NOW IS THE HOUR. THIS IS THE PLACE.

I'M PICKING UP UNCODED LOCAL TRANSMISSIONS. BATTLE DROID TRAFFIC.

WHAT ARE THEY ON ABOUT?

PADAWANS. THE MESSAGES ARE ABOUT PADAWANS.

I'M MONITORING COMM TRAFFIC THAT KEEPS REFERRING TO PADAWANS.

OUR MISSION IS COMPROMISED.

AS WE SUSPECTED.

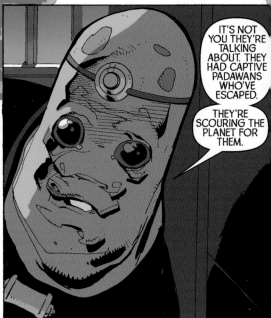

IT'S NOT YOU THEY'RE TALKING ABOUT. THEY HAD CAPTIVE PADAWANS WHO'VE ESCAPED.

THEY'RE SCOURING THE PLANET FOR THEM.

HOSTAGES?

GRIEVOUS HAS MADE NO DEMANDS.

WE TURNED OUR BACKS ON OUR TEACHING AND OUR DISCIPLINE TO SET OUT ON A MISSION OF VENGEANCE.

IT NOW BECOMES A MISSION OF MERCY.

HAS THIS BEEN HERE ALL THE TIME?

NO. IT LOOKS AS THOUGH THEY BUILT THIS RECENTLY.

AMAAAAAZING.

THEY HAVE FOOD, SHELTER, AND WATER ALL HIDDEN FROM THE GENERAL AND HIS DROIDS.

THIS MAY BE THE LAST OF THEM.

WHAT?

ALL OF THEIR PEOPLE ON THE SURFACE ARE DEAD.

NARGRA TELLE JEDI MAK!

THEY THINK WE'RE JEDI. THEY THINK WE CAN HELP THEM.

WE'RE ONLY PADAWANS--NOT YET KNIGHTS.

BUT HOW COULD THEY KNOW? THE FORCE DOESN'T RECOGNIZE SIZE.

WE'RE BIGGER THAN THEM. WE SEEM LIKE HEROES.

TO BE CONCLUDED

KILL THEM ALL. LET NOT A SINGLE ONE ESCAPE.

BUT LEAVE THE PADAWANS TO ME.

THEY'LL DIE AS THE JEDI THEY ASPIRE TO BE.

ALLARA! WHAT CAN WE DO?

WE FIGHT.

TO PROTECT OURSELVES AND OUR NEW FRIENDS.

THE UGNAUGHTS SAVED OUR LIVES.

WE MUST RETURN THEIR KINDNESS.

"VERY TROUBLESOME."

DROIDEKAS!

THEY'RE JUST BLOODY MACHINES!

≥UNH!≤ ≥UH!≤

KA-TOOM

THE WAY IS BLOCKED.

WE'LL FIND ANOTHER WAY AROUND.

NOT IN TIME TO SAVE THE PADAWANS.

THIS WAY. IT LEADS DEEPER INTO THE COMPLEX.

REMAIN IN THE LANDING AREA, STELLSKARD.

AND GRIEVOUS?

HE WON'T SURRENDER THE PADAWANS WHILE HE LIVES.

BACK TO THE SHIP. WE HOLD THERE.

IF THE JEDI FAIL, GRIEVOUS WILL COME TO US.

I CAN SENSE THEM. AM I WRONG?

YOU ARE NOT WRONG.

THEY ARE BELOW.

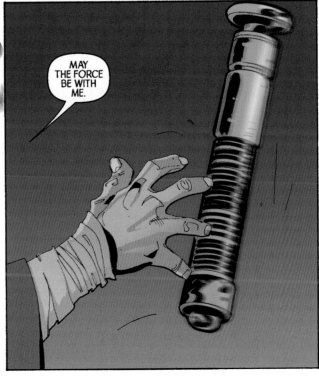

FOLLOW ME, PADAWANS. WE HAVE A SHIP TO TAKE YOU OFF-PLANET.

THERE'RE JUST A FEW HUNDRED BATTLEDROIDS BETWEEN US AND ESCAPE.

I'LL DO BETTER THAN FOLLOW.

I'LL FIGHT.

CAN MASTER TONE AND PADAWAN KYBO STOP GRIEVOUS?

THEY CAN STALL HIM.

"MAYBE LONG ENOUGH FOR US TO REACH THE RESCUE SHIP."

THERE ARE MORE COMING!

TRAIN THAT CANNON ON THEIR SAPPERS!

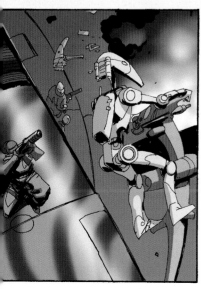

I'VE MASTERED YOUR WEAPON.

AND COMBINED THAT SKILL WITH THE SPEED ONLY A MACHINE IS CAPABLE OF.

HOW CAN ANY LIVING BEING STAND AGAINST ME?

ZKT

AND I HAVE RETURNED TO CORUSCANT TO BRING THE PADAWANS TO THE COUNCIL.

I LEAVE THEM IN YOUR CARE.

I WANT NOTHING FOR MYSELF.

I KNOW THAT, ALONG WITH MASTER TONE AND FLYNN KYBO, I VIOLATED MY VOW TO THE JEDI.

IS THERE NO MERCY FOR HIM?

NO. I WILL DEPART WITHOUT REGRET FOR MY ACTIONS.

MUCH TO REGRET YOU HAVE, CODI TY. THE BETRAYAL OF YOUR VOWS. THE DEATHS OF YOUR FRIENDS.

BANNED FROM THE JEDI ORDER YOU ARE. THE RESCUE OF THE PADAWANS, OUR JUDGMENT DOES NOT ALTER.

NOR DOES THE DEATH OF GENERAL GRIEVOUS...

"...IF, INDEED, HE IS DEAD."

END

LEONARDi
+
04 tennington